ABOUT THE 2STEVES

Steve Barlow was born in Crewe in the UK, and has worked at various times as a teacher, an actor, a stage manager and a puppeteer in England, and in Botswana, Africa. He met Steve Skidmore at a school in Nottingham and the 2Steves began writing together. Steve Barlow now lives in Somerset and sails a boat named Which Way, so called because he usually hasn't a clue where he's going.

Steve Skidmore is shorter and less hairy than Steve Barlow. After passing some exams at school, he went on to Nottingham University where he spent most of his time playing sport and doing a variety of heroic summer jobs, including counting pastry pie lids (honest). He trained as a teacher of Drama, English and Film Studies, before teaming up with Steve Barlow to become a full-time author.

Together they have written many books, including:
The Mad Myths series
Find out more at:
www.the2steves.net

ABOUT THE ILLUSTRATOR

Sonia Leong is based in Cambridge, in the UK, and is a superstar manga artist. She won Tokyopop's first UK Rising Stars of Manga competition (2005-06) and her first graphic novel was Manga Shakespeare: Romeo and Juliet. She's a member of Sweatdrop Studios and has too many awards to fit in this teeny space.
Find Sonia at her website: www.fyredrake.net

I HERO

Tomb Runner

Steve Barlow and Steve Skidmore
Illustrated by Sonia Leong

LONDON·SYDNEY

First published in 2010
by Franklin Watts

Text © Steve Barlow and Steve Skidmore 2010
Illustrations © Sonia Leong 2010
The "2Steves" illustrations by Paul Davidson
used by kind permission of Orchard Books
Cover design by Jonathan Hair

Franklin Watts
338 Euston Road
London NW1 3BH

Franklin Watts Australia
Level 17/207 Kent Street
Sydney, NSW 2000

A CIP catalogue record for this book
is available from the British Library.

ISBN: 978 0 7496 9679 5

1 3 5 7 9 10 8 6 4 2

Printed in Great Britain

Franklin Watts is a division of Hachette Children's Books,
an Hachette UK company.
www.hachette.co.uk

Decide your own destiny...

This book is not like others you may have read. *You* are the hero of this adventure. It is up to you to make decisions that will affect how the adventure unfolds.

Each section of this book is numbered. At the end of most sections, you will have to make a choice. The choice you make will take you to a different section of the book.

Some of your choices will help you to complete the adventure successfully. But choose carefully, some of your decisions could be fatal!

If you fail, then start the adventure again and learn from your mistake.

If you choose correctly you will succeed in your adventure.

Don't be a zero, be a hero!

You are one of the world's leading treasure hunters. Your talent for archaeology is only matched by your skills in martial arts and languages. You have travelled the world searching for, and discovering, priceless treasures and artefacts. Many of these adventures have been dangerous, but you have always succeeded in bringing back the archaeological treasures you set out to find. This has made you – and the charities you support – very rich.

In your latest quest you are trying to discover the hiding place of Blackbeard the Pirate's treasure. You are in your library, studying an antique map, when your butler enters. He coughs.

"What is it, Peters?" you ask.

"I'm sorry to disturb you," he replies, "but there is a gentleman in the lobby. He wishes to see you. He says it is very important. Here is his card."

J P GREENBACK JNR
COLLECTOR
DALLAS, TEXAS

"Interesting," you say. "J P Greenback – he's
an American who has made a fortune in oil.
He's used his money to put together one of the
world's greatest collections of ancient objects.
What does he want, I wonder? Show him in
Peters."

Now turn to section 1.

1

A few moments later, the library door opens and Peters shows in J P Greenback Jnr.

"Howdee," he says, shaking your hand. "JP's my name. It is a pleasure and a privilege to meet such a famous adventurer." He glances around your library. "Quite a collection, you have here."

"I have heard that yours is a greater one," you reply. "I believe you have a lot of money to spend on it."

Greenback smiles. "Money can't buy you everything. However, I believe it will help me to buy your services."

If are offended by Greenback's words, go to 20.

If you want to know how much Greenback wishes to offer, go to 49.

2

Before Sükh can react, you grab hold of his arm and stun him with a karate chop.

He staggers to his knees and drops the gun on the floor. You have to make an immediate decision. Should you reach for the gun or use your martial arts skills to defeat Sükh?

If you want to pick up the gun, go to 28.

If you decide to use your fighting skills, go to 42.

3

You drive slowly towards the ravine and edge the jeep onto the bridge. It creaks and rocks violently. You drive further onto the bridge.

Suddenly there is a loud crack as the ropes begin to snap. You have to make an immediate decision.

If you want to try and drive across the bridge at speed, go to 24.

If you decide to grab your bag and get out of the jeep, go to 45.

4

Greenback suddenly screams. The figure of a ghostly warrior emerges from the tomb, takes the sword out of his hand, and plunges it into his chest. More ghostly warriors follow, armed with swords.

As you look on in horror at the scene, the leader of the Guardians places his hand on your shoulder. "If you are of true heart, stay still," he says.

If you want to try and run away, go to 40.
If you decide to do as the leader of the Guardians says, go to 25.

5

Over the next day, you research more about Genghis Khan.

He was originally called Temüjin, and only took the name of Genghis Khan when he defeated his enemies and was made ruler of all the Mongols. Your research backs up Greenback's story about the location of the monastery in a hidden valley in Mongolia.

You try and find the hidden valley using satellite imagery on your computer. However, no matter what you do, you cannot get a clear picture of the location.

Very strange, you think, I wonder what is causing that…

Now go to 15.

6

The room is lined with wooden shelves on which lie many ancient manuscripts and maps. You realise that you have found the monastery's library. On the far wall of the room is a large prayer wheel.

If you wish to search for the manuscript that reveals the location of the tomb, go to 23.

If you wish to spin the prayer wheel, go to 37.

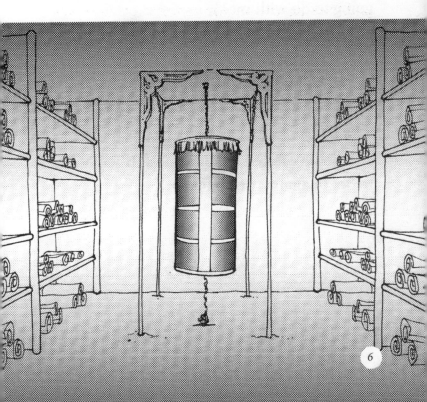

7

You wake up in a cold stone cell. Your hands and legs are chained to a wall. Several men dressed in black robes are standing over you.

"Who are you?" you ask.

One of the men steps forward. "We are the Guardians of the Tomb of Genghis Khan. We are sworn to keep it secret from the outside world."

You feel sick in your stomach. "What are you going to do with me?"

"Nothing. Quite literally."

They leave the cell, slamming the heavy wooden door shut and plunging you into darkness. You realise that you will never get out alive…

You have failed in your quest. If you wish to begin again, turn back to 1.

8

You hold up the glow stick, but it has no effect – the creature moves towards you. You struggle to free yourself from its web, but it is useless. You are stuck fast!

The creature's deadly jaws open and then snap shut, cutting off your cries forever.

You have failed. If you wish to try again, go back to 1.

9

"Tell me more," you say.

"Through a series of informants, I have discovered that there is a manuscript hidden in the library of a Buddhist monastery which tells exactly where the tomb is located. This monastery is in a secret valley in Northern Mongolia."

"If you know so much, why do you need me?" you ask. "Just go yourself."

Greenback shakes his head. "I do not wish to bring attention to the quest. The Mongolian authorities take a dim view of people trying to discover the location of the tomb and removing what treasures may lie within it. You have a reputation for secrecy and getting the job done. I need you…"

If you wish to take up this adventure, go to 32.

If you would prefer to stick to trying to discover Blackbeard's treasure, go to 43.

10

"You've been searching for the tomb of Genghis Khan, you should open the one that bears his name," you reply.

Greenback orders his men to open the tomb. They use crowbars to force off the lid and stand back to allow Greenback to look into the tomb.

He peers in, "There is no body in here. Just this." He pulls out a rusty sword.

"The sword of the Khan," says the leader of the Guardians of the Tomb. "To keep good men true and reward evil men with their just deserts."

Go to 4.

11

You continue along the ledge and soon reach the tunnel at the far side of the cavern.

You light another glow stick and make your way through the dark passage. After some time you see light ahead of you. You run towards it and step out into a valley, surrounded by snow-topped mountains. In the distance you see a monastery.

"This must be the hidden valley!" you mutter. "Now to find the manuscript!"

If you want to walk into the monastery, go to 41.

If you want to try and enter the monastery without being seen, go to 18.

12

You dive into the jeep, pulling the dead Sükh in with you to act as a shield. Bullets shatter the side window and door.

Frantically, you search through Sükh's pockets and find the keys to the jeep.

If you want to try to drive away immediately, go to 22.

If you want to wait for the firing to stop, go to 46.

13

You dive into the icy cold water and begin swimming towards the tunnel.

Suddenly the water churns up around you. Thousands of tiny carnivorous fish surround you and begin biting at you. You thrash about, trying to get away, but it is helpless – there are too many of them. Bit by bit they eat at your flesh. Your blood mixes with the black water and you sink into the cold depths.

You have failed. If you wish to begin again, turn back to 1.

14

Smiling, you walk up to the guards with your hands held out. "Excuse me, I seem to be lost," you say.

The guards looked confused at your sudden appearance. Before they can react you attack, knocking them unconscious.

Stepping over their bodies, you enter the room. It is empty except for a large prayer wheel standing in the middle of the room.

You hear a noise in the corridor.

If you want to leave the room, go to 28.

If you wish to spin the prayer wheel, go to 37.

15

Two days later, you set off for Mongolia. After a comfortable flight, you arrive at Chinggis Khan, the international airport for Ulan Bator.

You make your way to arrivals and are approached by a man.

"Welcome to Mongolia," he says. "I am Sükh, your guide. Please follow me to your vehicle."

If you wish to follow Sükh, go to 48.
If you don't trust him, go to 36.

16

You leave the room and pass by groups of captured Guardians being watched over by Greenback's men.

Using the manuscript's directions, Greenback and some of his group take you and the leader of the Guardians of the Tomb down into the cellars of the monastery.

Greenback orders the Guardians' leader to tell him where the entrance to the chamber is. To your surprise he points to a trapdoor in the floor. One of Greenback's men lifts it up.

If you want to take this opportunity to try to escape, go to 46.

If you want to go into the chamber, go to 44.

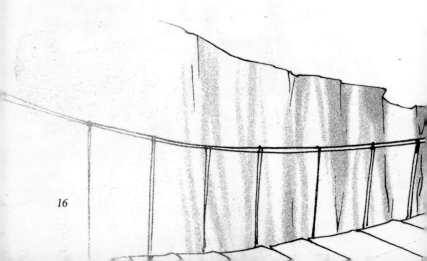

17

You pack your bag with essential supplies: the sat phone, climbing ropes, glow sticks and your pistol and ammunition. You leave the jeep and step out onto the bridge. The river rages far below and you see sharp rocks jutting upwards.

Just as you reach the halfway point, the bridge begins to shake violently. You look behind you and see a figure using a curved sword to chop at the ropes from which the wooden roadway hangs! Before you can reach for your gun, the bridge begins to break up.

If you want to sprint for the other side of the bridge, go to 24.

If you decide to wrap your arms around the bridge ropes and hang on, go to 45.

18

You decide to move around the edge of the valley before making your way towards the rear of the monastery.

Soon you are standing at the foot of the monastery wall.

Using a grappling rope from your pack, you climb up the wall and drop silently into the monastery. With your gun out, you make your way along an open corridor that has several doors leading off it.

Suddenly there is a sound of voices coming towards you. Two guards dressed in black robes appear. What should you do?

If you want to find somewhere to hide, go to 31.

If you want to order them to take you to their leader, go to 26.

If you want to run away from the guards, go to 28.

19

"You should open the one that says 'Temüjin'," you reply. "That was Genghis Khan's real name."

Greenback orders his men to open the tomb. They use crowbars to force off the lid and stand back to allow Greenback to look into the tomb.

He peers in, "I don't believe this," he cries out. They are the last words he utters…

Go to 40.

20

"Mr Greenback," you say angrily. "I do not care for your manner. I am offended by what you imply. You will apologise or I will ask Peters to show you the door."

Greenback looks embarrassed. "I am sorry, I didn't mean to annoy you. It is just my way. Please accept my apology."

You nod. "I do. Now what brings you here?"

"I have an adventure for you. However, it is dangerous – it will test you to your limits. But I will pay you handsomely if you choose to undertake it."

If you are more interested in the adventure than the money, go to 38.

If you are more interested in what you will be paid, go to 49.

21

The creature gets closer and you reach for your gun.

As the spider's deadly jaws open you aim your weapon into the blackness of its mouth and pull the trigger again and again. Bullets tear into its body and a nightmarish scream echoes around the cavern.

The spider falls into the water, which bubbles up into a churning whirlpool, before returning to a black stillness.

Breathing deeply, you free yourself from the web.

If you wish to continue making your way along the ledge, go to 11.

If you would now prefer to swim across to the tunnel, go to 13.

22

You push Sükh's body out of the vehicle. With bullets ripping into the bodywork, you start up the jeep, slam your foot onto the accelerator and speed off.

Soon you are out of range. Thankful for your escape, you drive on for some time. Once you have left Ulan Bator far behind you pull off the road to check the jeep.

It is full of the equipment you ordered – food, water, clothes, ropes, glow sticks… and an automatic pistol. You also check your bag to see whether the satellite phone is damaged. Luckily it isn't. You decide to head for the hidden valley.

Go to 39.

23

You begin to search through the manuscripts for the one that contains the location of the tomb. However, there are hundreds of them and you realise that this will take far too long: you will need someone to tell you where the manuscript is.

If you want to leave the library to look for help, go to 47.

If you think spinning the prayer wheel will help, go to 37.

24

You have made a fatal mistake! The ropes snap and you plunge down into the ravine, screaming with fear and the knowledge that you are about to die.

You have failed in your quest. If you wish to begin again, turn back to 1.

25

You remain still. Greenback's men panic and begin shooting, but their bullets have no effect on the ghostly warriors. Soon Greenback's men are all dead and the ghosts vanish again.

The leader of the Guardians turns to you. "They are the ghosts of the Mongol warriors, protecting their leader, Genghis Khan, and bringing death to all evil men. The Sword summoned them from their graves. It is as well that you are not a follower of he who took the sword: otherwise, you would be dead. Why did you choose to open that tomb?" he asks.

"I remembered the line in the manuscript," you reply. "The sword that conquered the world will bring destruction to evil men. I thought that Genghis Khan would be buried with the name he began with – Temüjin."

The leader nods. "Do you wish to open Temüjin's tomb and see what treasures lie there?"

You think of the money that you could make telling the world about the tomb.

If you wish to open the tomb, go to 33.
If you don't, go to 50.

26

You point your gun at the guards. "Take me to the head of this monastery," you repeat.

In reply, one of the guards kicks the gun from your hand and launches a fearsome attack. You fight back, using all your martial arts skills. You manage to knock out one of the guards, but the other one catches you with a stunning high kick to your head. You drop to the floor, unconscious.

Go to 7.

27

"Mr Greenback, Mongolia is a vast country – thousands of people have searched in vain for the tomb. It will never be found. I am far too busy to chase a fantasy."

Greenback shakes his head. "It is no fantasy, I am sure of the location of the tomb. And if you do not find it, I will still pay you."

If you wish to hear more about the location of the tomb, go to 9.

If you want to ask about what you will be paid, go to 49.

If you are not interested in the quest, go to 43.

28

As you turn away, you feel a searing pain at the base of your neck. You drop to the floor, unconscious.

Go to 7.

29

"How did you get here?" you ask Greenback. "The satellite phone I gave you has a tracking device in it," he replies. "My men and I have been following you from the moment you landed. I needed you to provide a distraction for these people."

He pushes forward a bald-headed man dressed in robes. "This is the head of this monastery and leader of the Guardians of the Tomb. My men have taken over the monastery and thanks to you, we will soon find the tomb of Genghis Khan and its treasure. I hope you won't refuse my invitation to join me?"

If you want to reach for your gun and shoot Greenback, go to 46.

If you agree to go along with Greenback, go to 16.

If you refuse to help Greenback, go to 34.

30

You climb the rope nearest the opening. However, this causes it to fray even more. Just as it is about to snap, you throw yourself to the side and grab hold of the bottom lip of the opening. Straining with all your might, you pull yourself into it.

Once you have recovered your breath, you reach into your bag, take out a glow stick and activate it. You head into the opening and realise that it leads into a tunnel. You walk on carefully and eventually arrive at a huge cavern with a lake. Lighting another glow stick, you can just make out a small ledge running around the lake which leads to another tunnel on the far side.

If you want to balance on the ledge around the side of the lake, go to 35.

If you want to swim across the lake to the tunnel, go to 13.

31

You open one of the doors on the corridor
and quickly slip inside.

You wait at the door, listening carefully.
You hear the guards pass by. What should
you do now?

If you wish to explore this room, go to 6.
If you wish to leave the room, go to 47.

32

"I'm interested," you say. "Tell me more."

Greenback smiles. "The monastery is in a
secret valley in the Khentii mountains, north-
east of the Mongolian capital, Ulan Bator.

"You'll travel there and find the manuscript.
If you can decode it, you should discover the
location of the tomb. When you do, I want to
know immediately and I will join you as soon
as I can." He reaches into a bag and hands over
a satellite phone. "Use this. It will scramble the
message. I don't trust normal communication.
Other people might be listening."

You wonder who the 'others' might be, but
say nothing.

"In the meantime, I will make travel arrangements. A guide will meet you at the airport. His name is Jamuka. He will supply you with all your equipment."

Over the next hour you give Greenback a list of your requirements. Finally, he shakes your hand. "Hopefully, I will see you when you have discovered the tomb of Genghis Khan." Peters shows him to the door.

If you wish to find out more about Genghis Khan, go to 5.

If you wish to get on with your adventure, go to 15.

33

"I would love to," you reply.

"Then you are only a thief after all," replies the leader.

The air is once again filled with ghostly warriors, all with their weapons ready. One ghoulish figure speeds toward you. You scream and scream as its sword hacks at your body…

You failed the final test. If you wish to begin again, go back to 1.

34

"I'm not helping you any more," you say.

"Very well," replies Greenback, "I don't need you anymore."

The last sight you see is Greenbacks' men raising their weapons. The last sound you hear is the crack of the bullets heading towards your body…

Your adventure is over. If you wish to begin again, go to 1.

35

You hold the glow stick in your teeth, and begin to balance around on the narrow ledge.

As you move across, you feel a sticky, hair-like substance brush against your face. You continue on, but the strands become thicker and stickier, pulling at your body and entangling you.

As you try to struggle through, there is a blood curdling noise above you. You look up and your blood turns cold – it is a monstrous spider, heading towards you. You have wandered into its web!

If you want to escape by diving into the water, go to 13.

If you want to attack the spider, go to 21.

If you want to use the glow stick to frighten it off, go to 8.

36

"Where is Jamuka?" you ask.

Sükh shakes his head. "He has met with an accident. I am his replacement. Do not worry, I have all your equipment. It is in a jeep in the car park."

If you decide to follow Sükh, go to 48.
If you don't wish to follow him, go to 28.

37

You spin the prayer wheel. To your amazement a secret door opens in the wall.

You light a glow stick and enter a small room. There is a table on which lies an ancient manuscript. You begin to read it and realise that it is the manuscript that you have been searching for! It tells you that the tomb you are looking for is located in a chamber beneath the monastery.

You are puzzled by one of the lines in the manuscript. You read it out: "The sword that conquered the world will bring destruction to evil men." You wonder what it means.

Picking up the manuscript, you turn to leave

the room, but a familiar voice makes you gasp
and stop dead in your tracks.

"Well done! First you found the valley
and now the manuscript. Now all we have to
find is the tomb!" Standing at the door is J P
Greenback with a group of armed men!

Go to 29.

38

"As you can see, I am not poor," you say. "I am more interested in adventure."

"I am glad to hear it," replies Greenback. "Then I will tell you why I have come here. I am sure you know about the legend of the tomb of Genghis Khan?"

In reply, you reach into a drawer and pull out a large map. You place it on your desk and unfurl it.

You point at the map. "Genghis Khan founded the Mongol Empire in the thirteenth

century. He was a great warrior and united the tribes of Central Asia. He died in 1227 and was buried somewhere in Mongolia. His tomb has never been found, although many people have searched for it… and usually ended up dead," you add. "The legend of the tomb is just a story. No one will ever find it."

"Don't be so sure," Greenback replies. "I have obtained information about its location."

If you wish to hear more, go to 9.
If you think Greenback is wasting your time, go to 27.

39

You program your sat nav with the location of the hidden valley and begin your drive across the Mongolian plains.

Hours later, the terrain becomes more mountainous. Following your sat nav, you drive up a dirt track and eventually arrive at a deep ravine. There is a wooden bridge spanning the gap. You check on the sat nav – there is no way around. You will have to cross the bridge.

You assess the situation – the bridge is wide enough for the jeep, but will it take the weight?

If you decide to drive across, go to 3.

If you decide to leave the jeep and travel on foot, go to 17.

40

The chamber fills with hundreds of armed ghostly figures pouring out of the tomb.

Your mind suddenly realises who they are – the ghosts of the Mongol warriors, protecting their leader, Genghis Khan, and bringing death to all intruders.

Your last sight is of a ghostly sword plunging into your body and your very real blood pouring onto the floor.

Your adventure is over. If you wish to begin again, go to 1.

41

You make your way to the monastery entrance. You are stopped at the gate by two guards dressed in dark robes.

You bow and in perfect Mongolian say, "I would like to speak to the head of your monastery."

One of the guards shakes his head. "Go away stranger. You should not be here."

If you want to try to find a different way into the monastery, go to 28.

If you decide to threaten them with your gun, go to 26.

42

You leap at Sükh and hold his head in a chinlock. "Where is Jamuka and who are you working for?" you demand. "Tell me or I will break your neck."

"Let me go and I will tell you," gasps Sükh. You release him a little, still keeping a firm grip on him. But before he can say anything you hear a gunshot. He slumps forward, dead. Blood seeps from his forehead.

More shots ring out, hitting the ground around you. You have to get out of this situation!

If you choose to jump into the jeep, go to 12.

If you want to run back to the airport building, go to 28.

43

You shake your head. "I am sorry, I am not interested in this fantasy. I have more real treasures to seek."

Peters shows Mr Greenback to the door.

Your adventure is over before it began. If you would like to start again, return to 1.

44

Greenback and his men take you and the Leader of the Guardians into the chamber. It is lit up by flaming torches. In the centre of the chamber are two stone tombs.

Greenback inspects them and calls you over. "You're the expert," he says, "why are there two tombs?"

You translate the inscriptions. "The one on the left says 'Here lies Temüjin', the one on the right says, 'Here lies Genghis Khan – the conquering sword.' I don't know what that means," you tell Greenback.

"Which one should we open first?" he asks. You recall the line in the manuscript that puzzled you: 'The sword that conquered the world will bring destruction to evil men.'

If you think you should open the tomb that says 'Temüjin', go to 19.

If you think you should open the one that says 'Genghis Khan', go to 10.

If you refuse to have anything more to do with Greenback, go to 34.

45

You leap for the rope that supports the bridge and wrap your arm tightly around it. Seconds later the bridge gives way, sending you hurtling towards the opposite cliff face.

You crash into the rock wall but manage to hold on. Swinging on the rope, you look around you. Below you, the river rages, but to your left there seems to be a small opening in the cliff.

The bridge judders again – the ropes above you are beginning to fray. You have to get out of here quickly!

If you want to climb up and out of the ravine, go to 24.

If you wish to try to reach the opening in the cliff, go to 30.

45

46

You have made a mistake! A stream of bullets rip into your body. You scream in pain before slipping into oblivion.

You have failed in your adventure. If you wish to begin again, go to 1.

47

You open the door and make your way down the corridor. You turn a corner and see two men standing guard outside a room. This room is obviously important!

If you wish to try to trick your way into the room, go to 14.

If you want to force the guards to let you into the room, go to 26.

If you decide to go back along the corridor, go to 28.

48

You follow Sükh out of the airport and into the car park where your jeep is waiting for you. Sükh opens the door and suddenly spins around. You gasp – he is pointing a gun at your chest!

"Get in and do not make a sound," he orders.

If you try to resist being kidnapped, go to 2.
If you decide to do as he says, go to 28.

49

"How much are you offering?" you ask. "I will need to be paid a lot of money."

Greenback shakes his head. "You have failed my test. I want someone who values adventure and discovery more than money. You are not that person. Goodbye."

He marches out of the room. You realise that your greed has lost you the chance of taking part in a great adventure.

If you wish to begin again, go to 1.

50

"The Tomb of Temüjin will remain here undisturbed," you say. "And I promise that I will not betray this great secret."

The leader of the Guardians nods. "You have chosen wisely. I will order my people to escort you from our valley. To be a hero does not only mean doing brave deeds, but also making brave and noble choices. The choice you have made is a truly noble one and you are a true hero!"

ARTIST AT WORK!

Hi there! I'm Sonia, and I draw all the artwork in the I HERO books. I work mainly as a manga artist and I run drawing workshops, too.

I draw in three main stages for I HERO. First, I sketch out the rough positions in pencil. Then I make any changes and work up the art in ink. Finally, I add layers of texture for the fills and shadows.

This is the art from section 15, where you arrive at the airport. You can see where I was asked to add a taxi rank outside.

1.

This is the art from section 4, where Greenback is killed. I changed the rough here as the ghost's sword arm wasn't quite right.

2.

Want the chance to see your I HERO fan art* in an I HERO book? Send it to:

**I HERO fan art
EDGE/Franklin Watts
15th Floor, 338 Euston Road,
London NW1 3BH**

or email it to:

ad@hachettechildrens.co.uk

Dragon Slayer

Steve Barlow and Steve Skidmore

Illustrated by Sonia Leong

You are a warrior from the land of Scanda.
Lord Danu is the ruler of your people.

You are a monster slayer. You have fought
wolves and wild boars, the walrus and the
killer whale, brown bears of the forests and
white bears of the snow-lands. You have
battled against ogres and giants. But you have
never yet tested your strength against the
creature that all your people fear – a dragon.

Your latest mission was to slay a giant. You
are sailing home in your longship bearing its
head as a trophy for your Lord. Though both
you and your men are weary, you are pleased
with your success.

Continue reading the adventure in
I HERO Dragon Slayer

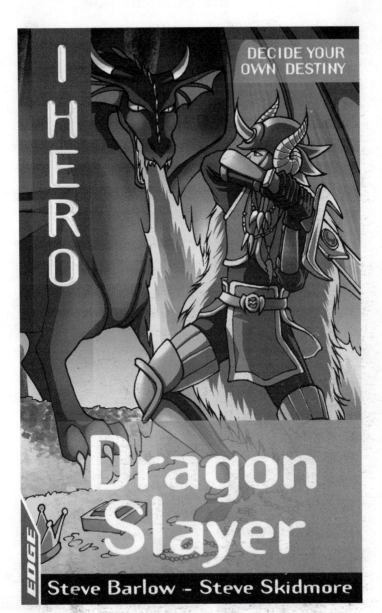

All these other I, HERO titles are available now!

I HERO

Dragon Slayer
Steve Barlow - Steve Skidmore

978 0 7496 9678 8

Strike Force
Steve Barlow - Steve Skidmore

978 0 7496 9036 6

Pirate Gold
Steve Barlow - Steve Skidmore

978 0 7496 8264 4

Space Rescue
Steve Barlow - Steve Skidmore

978 0 7496 9035 9

Save the Empire!
Steve Barlow - Steve Skidmore

978 0 7496 8265 1

Code Mission
Steve Barlow - Steve Skidmore

978 0 7496 7667 4

Death or Glory!
Steve Barlow - Steve Skidmore

978 0 7496 7664 3

Gorgon's Cave
Steve Barlow - Steve Skidmore

978 0 7496 7666 7

Viking Blood
Steve Barlow - Steve Skidmore

978 0 7496 7665 0